G000153556

Skills Builders

Fractions, Decimals and Percentages

YEAR 6

Richard Cooper and Karen Hamilton

RISING STARS

Rising Stars UK Ltd, 7 Hatchers Mews, Bermondsey Street, London SE1 3GS
www.risingstars-uk.com

Every effort has been made to trace copyright holders and obtain their permission for the use of copyright materials. The publishers will gladly receive information enabling them to rectify any error or omission in subsequent editions.

All facts are correct at time of going to press.

Published 2013
Text, design and layout © 2013 Rising Stars UK Ltd

Project manager: Dawn Booth
Editorial: David Hemsley
Proofreader: Bobby Francis
Design: Words & Pictures, London
Cover design: Amina Dudhia
Character illustration: Louisa Burville-Riley

British Library Cataloguing-in-Publication Data
A CIP record for this book is available from the British Library.

ISBN 978-0-85769-692-2
Printed in Singapore by Craft Print International Limited

Skills Builders: Fractions, Decimals and Percentages

YEAR 6

Contents

How to use this book

The *Skills Builders Fractions, Decimals and Percentages* series is designed to help you get to grips with this tricky topic.

The key thing to remember about fractions, decimals and percentages is:

> They are all different ways of expressing the same amount.

For example: 25% is the same as $\frac{1}{4}$ which is also the same as 0.25.

1 The introduction to each section gives you an idea of the sort of problems you are likely to see and helps you to understand what maths you need to use.

2 The flow chart takes you through an example problem step-by-step. This is important when you are answering questions about fractions, decimals and percentages.

3 The hints and tips section gives you useful ideas for completing the problems on the following page. These are the things you need to remember if you are doing a quiz or test!

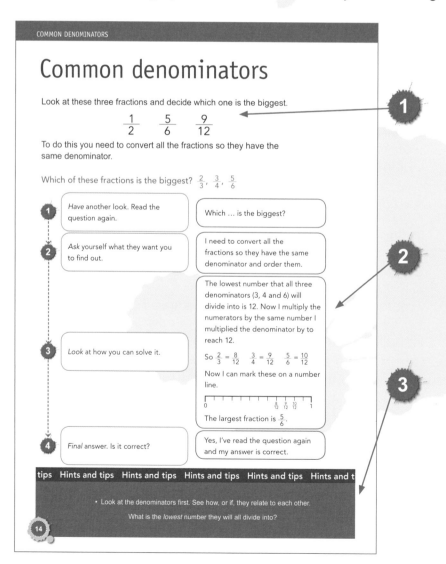

The questions get harder as you go down the page.

4 Section 1 questions are fairly straightforward and help you to practise your skills.

5 Section 2 questions are a bit harder but will help you to remember all the key points.

6 The Challenge sections are really tough and sometimes mean that you can make up games and your own questions. They can be great fun!

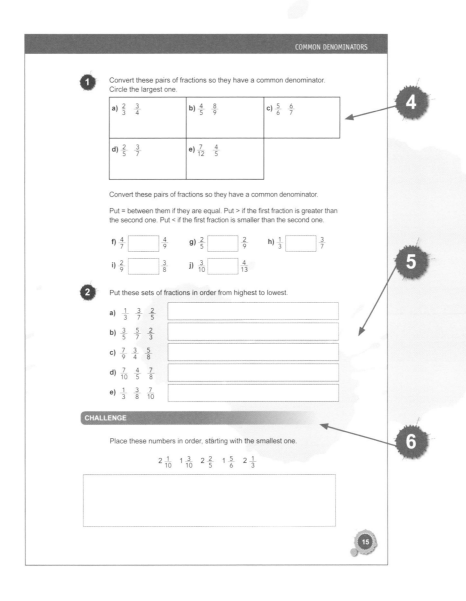

Ten top tips

1 Work through each question step-by-step. Follow the flow chart.

Every time you approach a fractions question, remember these four steps

Have another look. Read the question again.

Ask yourself what they want you to find out.

Look at how you can solve it.

Final answer. Is it correct?

We can remember this by looking at the first letter of each step.

They read HALF!

2 Always *show your working or 'method'*. This will help you to keep track of what you have done and may help you to get extra marks.

3 Always *include your units* in the answer. If you don't, you won't get full marks.

4 When you first read through a question, *underline important words and numbers*. This will help you to remember the important bits!

5 *Draw a picture* to help you. Sometimes a question is easier if you can 'see' it.

Drawing 6 apples can help you if you need to divide them!

6 If the problem has a number of steps, break it down and *do one step at a time.*

7 When *checking your answers*, look at the inverse operation.

8 Sometimes an answer will 'sound right'. Read it out (quietly) and listen. *Does it make sense?*

9 If you are using measurements (grams, litres, cm), make sure that the *units are the same* before you calculate.

10 Once again! *Remember the mnemonic HALF.*

Changing improper fractions to mixed numbers

An improper fraction is a fraction where the denominator (bottom number) is bigger than the numerator (top number).

You need to be able to change these to a 'mixed number'. Mixed numbers are whole numbers and fractions together.

$\frac{33}{8}$ as a mixed number is 4 and $\frac{1}{8}$.

8 fits into 33 four times with one eighth left over. We write this as 4 $\frac{1}{8}$.

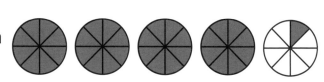

Change the improper fraction $\frac{37}{10}$ to a mixed number.

1 *Have* another look. Read the question again.

Improper fraction …
mixed number …

2 *Ask* yourself what they want you to find out.

Change 37 tenths into a mixed number …

3 *Look* at how you can solve it.

37 divided by 10 is 3 with 7 remaining.

4 *Final* answer. Is it correct?

3 $\frac{7}{10}$. Yes, that is the correct mixed number.

1 Turn these improper fractions into mixed numbers.

a) $\frac{15}{4}$

b) $\frac{62}{6}$

c) $\frac{31}{3}$

d) $\frac{56}{13}$

e) $\frac{46}{5}$

f) $\frac{34}{11}$

g) $\frac{63}{8}$

h) $\frac{77}{9}$

i) $\frac{41}{13}$

j) $\frac{100}{18}$

2 Now turn these mixed numbers into improper fractions.

a) $7 \frac{3}{8}$

b) $72 \frac{9}{13}$

c) $27 \frac{3}{7}$

d) $91 \frac{1}{9}$

e) $53 \frac{5}{6}$

CHALLENGE

a) Seven and a quarter pizzas were eaten at Laura's party. How many twelfths of pizza were eaten in total?

b) Fourteen and a third cream cakes were eaten for dessert! How many sixths of cream cake is this in total?

c) Dad said he would give me $\frac{9}{5}$ of £5 or £6.50 if I washed the car. Which one is the greater? By how much?

Relationships between fractions

Look at these fraction bars.

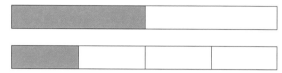

They show that $\frac{1}{2}$ is twice as much as one quarter.

Now look at this bar.

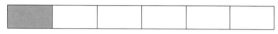

$\frac{1}{2}$ is three times as much as $\frac{1}{6}$.

Complete this sentence: $\frac{1}{4}$ is twice as much as …

1 *Have* another look. Read the question again.

Twice as much …

2 *Ask* yourself what they want you to find out.

I need to find what is half of $\frac{1}{4}$.

I need to draw a picture here.

First colour in $\frac{1}{4}$ of one.

Now I must colour in $\frac{1}{2}$ of $\frac{1}{4}$.

That must be $\frac{1}{8}$.

3 *Look* at how you can solve it.

4 *Final* answer. Is it correct?

Check the drawing. Is it correct? Yes! I've got it right.

tips   Hints and tips   Hints and tips   Hints and tips   Hints and tips   Hints and t

- Think about the links.

$\frac{1}{2}$ is twice as much as $\frac{1}{4}$. $\frac{1}{4}$ is twice as much as $\frac{1}{8}$.

The larger the denominator, the smaller the fraction.

10

1 Look at these fractions.

Write 'twice as much as' or 'half as much as' in the spaces.

Draw fraction bars to solve these.

a) $\frac{1}{4}$ [_____] $\frac{1}{2}$

b) $\frac{1}{4}$ [_____] $\frac{1}{8}$

c) $\frac{1}{5}$ [_____] $\frac{1}{10}$

d) $\frac{1}{3}$ [_____] $\frac{1}{6}$

e) $\frac{1}{20}$ [_____] $\frac{1}{10}$

f) $\frac{1}{8}$ is half as much as [____]

[_____]

g) $\frac{1}{10}$ is twice as much as [____]

[_____]

h) $\frac{1}{2}$ is ten times as much as [____]

[_____]

i) $\frac{1}{3}$ is three times as much as [____]

[_____]

2 Complete these number sentences.

a) $\frac{2}{5}$ is twice as much as [____]

b) $\frac{3}{4}$ is twice as much as [____]

c) $\frac{1}{10}$ is ten times as much as [____]

d) $\frac{1}{100}$ is half as much as [____]

e) $\frac{1}{20}$ is half as much as [____]

CHALLENGE

a) I have 12 drinks on a tray. $\frac{1}{6}$ of the drinks are lemonade. There are twice as many cola as lemonade. What fraction of the drinks are cola?

[_____]

b) I have 16 doughnuts in a bag. $\frac{1}{2}$ are jam and there are four times as many jam as vanilla. What fraction of the doughnuts are vanilla?

[_____]

Reducing fractions – cancelling

Look at this fraction equivalent statement: $\frac{2}{3} = \frac{8}{12}$

We can reduce a fraction down to its simplest form by finding a number which divides exactly into the top and bottom number.

$\frac{8}{12}$ can be made simpler by dividing the numerator and the denominator by 4.

$8 \div 4 = 2$ $12 \div 4 = 3$ So $\frac{8}{12} = \frac{2}{3}$

Reduce this fraction to its lowest possible form: $\frac{12}{16}$

1 *Have* another look. Read the question again.

Reduce … $\frac{12}{16}$ …

2 *Ask* yourself what they want you to find out.

I need to reduce the fraction $\frac{12}{16}$ to its lowest form.

3 *Look* at how you can solve it.

What is the highest number that divides into 12 and 16? OK, 4. 12 divided by 4 is 3 and 16 divided by 4 is 4. The answer is $\frac{3}{4}$.

4 *Final* answer. Is it correct?

Yes, I've read the question again and my answer is correct.

1   Reduce these fractions to their lowest form.

a) $\frac{9}{12}$ b) $\frac{15}{25}$

c) $\frac{10}{20}$ d) $\frac{12}{48}$

e) $\frac{8}{10}$ f) $\frac{14}{24}$

g) $\frac{6}{18}$ h) $\frac{16}{48}$

i) $\frac{7}{21}$ j) $\frac{18}{24}$

2   Reduce these fractions to their simplest form.

a) $\frac{45}{54}$

b) $\frac{75}{195}$

c) $\frac{12}{96}$

d) $\frac{96}{336}$

e) $\frac{69}{108}$

CHALLENGE

Write down 5 equivalent fractions for each of the following. However, none of your equivalents are allowed to be double the previous one.

a) $\frac{1}{3}$

b) $\frac{1}{5}$

c) $\frac{8}{7}$

d) $\frac{5}{8}$

Common denominators

Look at these three fractions and decide which one is the biggest.

$$\frac{1}{2} \qquad \frac{5}{6} \qquad \frac{9}{12}$$

To do this you need to convert all the fractions so they have the same denominator.

Which of these fractions is the biggest? $\frac{2}{3}$, $\frac{3}{4}$, $\frac{5}{6}$

1 *Have* another look. Read the question again.

Which … is the biggest?

2 *Ask* yourself what they want you to find out.

I need to convert all the fractions so they have the same denominator and order them.

3 *Look* at how you can solve it.

The lowest number that all three denominators (3, 4 and 6) will divide into is 12. Now I multiply the numerators by the same number I multiplied the denominator by to reach 12.

So $\frac{2}{3} = \frac{8}{12}$ $\frac{3}{4} = \frac{9}{12}$ $\frac{5}{6} = \frac{10}{12}$

Now I can mark these on a number line.

0 $\frac{8}{12}$ $\frac{9}{12}$ $\frac{10}{12}$ 1

The largest fraction is $\frac{5}{6}$.

4 *Final* answer. Is it correct?

Yes, I've read the question again and my answer is correct.

tips Hints and tips Hints and tips Hints and tips Hints and tips Hints and t

- Look at the denominators first. See how, or if, they relate to each other.

What is the *lowest* number they will all divide into?

1 Convert these pairs of fractions so they have a common denominator. Circle the largest one.

a) $\frac{2}{3}$ $\frac{3}{4}$	b) $\frac{4}{5}$ $\frac{8}{9}$	c) $\frac{5}{6}$ $\frac{6}{7}$
d) $\frac{2}{5}$ $\frac{3}{7}$	e) $\frac{7}{12}$ $\frac{4}{5}$	

Convert these pairs of fractions so they have a common denominator.

Put = between them if they are equal. Put > if the first fraction is greater than the second one. Put < if the first fraction is smaller than the second one.

f) $\frac{4}{7}$ ☐ $\frac{4}{9}$ g) $\frac{2}{5}$ ☐ $\frac{2}{9}$ h) $\frac{1}{3}$ ☐ $\frac{3}{7}$

i) $\frac{2}{9}$ ☐ $\frac{3}{8}$ j) $\frac{3}{10}$ ☐ $\frac{4}{13}$

2 Put these sets of fractions in order from highest to lowest.

a) $\frac{1}{3}$ $\frac{3}{7}$ $\frac{2}{5}$ ☐

b) $\frac{3}{5}$ $\frac{5}{7}$ $\frac{2}{3}$ ☐

c) $\frac{7}{9}$ $\frac{3}{4}$ $\frac{5}{8}$ ☐

d) $\frac{7}{10}$ $\frac{4}{5}$ $\frac{7}{8}$ ☐

e) $\frac{1}{3}$ $\frac{3}{8}$ $\frac{7}{10}$ ☐

CHALLENGE

Place these numbers in order, starting with the smallest one.

$2\frac{1}{10}$ $1\frac{3}{10}$ $2\frac{2}{5}$ $1\frac{5}{6}$ $2\frac{1}{3}$

Adding and subtracting fractions with different denominators and mixed numbers

$3\frac{2}{5}$ is a mixed number because it is a mix of a whole number and a fraction. We say 'three and two fifths'.

What is the total of $4\frac{2}{5}$ and $6\frac{1}{5}$?

1 *Have* another look. Read the question again.

Four and two fifths *plus* six and one fifth.

2 *Ask* yourself what they want you to find out.

I need to find the total of the whole numbers and the total of the fractions.

Then I need to put them together.

3 *Look* at how you can solve it.

$4 + 6 = 10$

$\frac{2}{5} + \frac{1}{5} = \frac{3}{5}$

$10 + \frac{3}{5} = 10\frac{3}{5}$

The answer is 'ten and three fifths'.

4 *Final* answer. Is it correct?

Yes. I have checked my answer twice and it looks correct.

tips Hints and tips Hints and tips Hints and tips Hints and tips Hints and t

- If the fractions have different denominators it is easier to change one or both denominators so that they are the same. E.g. for the sum $\frac{3}{4} + \frac{3}{8}$ the lowest number that froth denominators will divide into is 8. $\frac{3}{8}$ stays the same. To change $\frac{3}{4}$ to eighths multiply the denominator by 2. Whatever is done to the denominator must also be done to the numerator: $\frac{3 \times 2}{4 \times 2} = \frac{6}{8}$

1 Add or subtract these mixed numbers.

a) $5\frac{5}{8} + 3\frac{1}{8}$

h) $6\frac{7}{8} - 1\frac{1}{8}$

b) $4\frac{3}{7} + 8\frac{2}{7}$

You'll need to change the following fractions into improper fractions.

c) $7\frac{6}{7} + 4\frac{1}{7}$

i) $7\frac{2}{7} - 4\frac{5}{7}$

d) $12\frac{2}{5} + 13\frac{2}{5}$

j) $12\frac{2}{5} - 11\frac{4}{5}$

e) $7\frac{3}{5} + 9\frac{2}{5}$

k) $13\frac{1}{9} - 11\frac{5}{9}$

f) $6\frac{2}{3} - 4\frac{1}{3}$

g) $9\frac{5}{6} - 8\frac{1}{6}$

2 Add or subtract these mixed numbers. Remember to change the denominators so that they are the same.

a) $\frac{5}{6} + \frac{7}{12}$

b) $\frac{3}{16} + \frac{7}{8}$

c) $\frac{10}{15} + \frac{4}{5}$

d) $\frac{11}{12} - \frac{5}{6}$

e) $\frac{7}{10} - \frac{9}{20}$

f) $\frac{3}{5} - \frac{3}{10}$

CHALLENGE

Dunya owns a cake shop. She sells cakes by the slice. On Monday she sells 6 and $\frac{3}{4}$ cakes, on Tuesday she sells 7 and $\frac{5}{8}$ cakes and on Wednesday 10 and $\frac{5}{16}$ cakes. How many cakes does she sell altogether?

Multiplying simple unit fractions by fractions

Multiplying fractions is easy. There are 3 simple steps:

1 Multiply the numerators

2 Multiply the denominators

3 Reduce (simplify) the fraction to its lowest form

Remember that a unit fraction is a fraction in which the numerator is *one*:

$$\frac{1}{2}, \ \frac{1}{3}, \ \frac{1}{4}, \ \frac{1}{7} \ \ldots$$

What is $\frac{1}{4} \times \frac{2}{5}$?

1 | *Have* another look. Read the question again. | One quarter multiplied by two fifths …

2 | *Ask* yourself what they want you to find out. | I need to find the product of the numerators and then calculate the product of the denominators.

3 | *Look* at how you can solve it. |
$$\frac{1}{4} \times \frac{2}{5} =$$
$$\frac{\text{Product of the numerators}}{\text{Product of the denominators}}$$
$$= \frac{1 \times 2}{4 \times 5} = \frac{2}{20}$$
Now reduce $\frac{2}{20} = \frac{1}{10}$
The answer is 'one tenth'.

4 | *Final* answer. Is it correct? | Yes. I have checked my answer twice and it looks correct.

tips   Hints and tips   Hints and tips   Hints and tips   Hints and tips   Hints and t

- When reducing a fraction, try to think of the highest common factor, i.e. the *highest* number that will divide exactly into both the numerator and the denominator. This will save you time as you will only need to divide once.

1 Multiply these unit fractions by non-unit fractions.

a) $\frac{1}{8} \times \frac{3}{4}$

b) $\frac{1}{7} \times \frac{2}{3}$

c) $\frac{9}{10} \times \frac{1}{2}$

d) $\frac{3}{5} \times \frac{1}{6}$

e) $\frac{1}{12} \times \frac{7}{4}$

2 Now multiply these proper fractions.

a) $\frac{3}{7} \times \frac{5}{6}$

b) $\frac{8}{9} \times \frac{2}{3}$

c) $\frac{4}{6} \times \frac{7}{10}$

d) $\frac{5}{12} \times \frac{11}{14}$

e) $\frac{10}{16} \times \frac{4}{5}$

3 Now have a go at multiplying these pairs of proper fractions. Remember to reduce the answers if necessary.

a) $\frac{5}{6} \times \frac{2}{3}$

b) $\frac{3}{8} \times \frac{4}{5}$

c) $\frac{4}{12} \times \frac{3}{4}$

d) $\frac{1}{16} \times \frac{4}{10}$

e) $\frac{7}{15} \times \frac{5}{14}$

CHALLENGE

Have a go at multiplying these mixed numbers. (Hint: Convert them to improper fractions first.)

a) $4\frac{3}{6} \times 1\frac{1}{6} =$

b) $3\frac{4}{7} \times 3\frac{3}{5} =$

c) $2\frac{7}{12} \times 3\frac{1}{4} =$

Dividing proper fractions by whole numbers

When you divide a fraction by a whole number you multiply the denominator (bottom number) by the whole number.

$$\frac{1}{2} \div 5 = \frac{1}{2 \times 5} = \frac{1}{10}$$

What would this look like in real life?

If half of a cake was divided into 5 equal slices this is what it would look like:

What is $\frac{1}{3} \div 8$?

1 *Have* another look. Read the question again.

... $\frac{1}{3}$ divided by 8 ...

2 *Ask* yourself what they want you to find out.

I want to divide one third into eight equal pieces. My answer will be smaller than a third.

3 *Look* at how you can solve it.

$$\frac{1}{3} \div 8$$
$$\frac{1}{3 \times 8} = \frac{1}{24}$$

This fraction cannot be simplified. So the answer is 'one twenty-fourth'.

4 *Final* answer. Is it correct?

I have visualised by drawing a cake. First I split it into thirds, then I split each third into 8 equal slices. There are 24 slices. Each slice is one twenty-fourth.

tips   Hints and tips   Hints and tips   Hints and tips   Hints and tips   Hints and t

- Visualising or drawing the whole as a cake or a pizza can help you to work out and check your answer.

1 Divide these fractions by whole numbers.

Now try these. You will need to simplify (cancel) the answers.

a) $\frac{1}{2} \div 3$

g) $\frac{3}{5} \div 6$

b) $\frac{2}{3} \div 5$

h) $\frac{4}{7} \div 8$

c) $\frac{3}{4} \div 2$

i) $\frac{2}{3} \div 14$

d) $\frac{5}{8} \div 6$

j) $\frac{6}{13} \div 12$

e) $\frac{1}{7} \div 9$

f) $\frac{7}{10} \div 8$

2 Can you work out the missing numbers?

a) $\frac{4}{9} \div$ ⬚ $= \frac{4}{27}$

b) $\frac{5}{7} \div$ ⬚ $= \frac{5}{28}$

Hint: The next two answers have been simplified.

c) $\frac{2}{3} \div$ ⬚ $= \frac{1}{6}$

d) $\frac{3}{4} \div$ ⬚ $= \frac{1}{8}$

CHALLENGE

It is Cassia's birthday. She cuts her cake into thirds and gives one third to her best friend Khadija. She shares the rest equally between eight of her classmates. What fraction of the whole cake does each of these classmates get? Hint: You might find it useful to draw a circle to represent the cake.

Decimal notation

Look at this number: 42.793. Each digit represents a number depending which column it is in.

42.793

The first column to the right of the decimal point is the tenths column.

The second column to the right of the decimal point is the hundredths column.

The third column to the right of the decimal point is the thousandths column.

Perform this calculation. Line up the digits in the correct columns.

372.7 + 61.89

1 _Have_ another look. Read the question again.

372.7 + 61.89 … It's addition.

2 _Ask_ yourself what they want you to find out.

I need to add them together and make sure I line up the digits and decimal points correctly.

3 _Look_ at how you can solve it.

Estimate an answer first:
370 + 60 = 430
(It will be easier if I add a zero to the .7 so I have the same amount of digits in each column.) 372.70
                                                    +   61.89
                                                    ────────
                                                      434.59

4 _Final_ answer. Is it correct?

Yes, my answer is close to my estimate. I have lined the digits up in the correct columns.

tips   Hints and tips   Hints and tips   Hints and tips   Hints and tips   Hints and t

- Start by lining up the decimal points and then write in the digits for the calculation.
- Adding a zero (or zeros) to level the number of digits in each column is a very useful way to avoid simple errors when calculating.

Answers

Skills Builders

Fractions, Decimals and Percentages

YEAR
6

Richard Cooper
and Karen Hamilton

Changing improper fractions to mixed numbers (page 9)

1 a) $3\frac{3}{4}$ **b)** $10\frac{1}{3}$ **c)** $10\frac{1}{3}$
d) $4\frac{4}{13}$ **e)** $9\frac{1}{5}$ **f)** $3\frac{1}{11}$ **g)** $7\frac{7}{8}$
h) $8\frac{5}{9}$ **i)** $3\frac{2}{13}$ **j)** $5\frac{5}{9}$

2 a) $\frac{59}{8}$ **b)** $\frac{945}{13}$ **c)** $\frac{192}{7}$ **d)** $\frac{820}{9}$ **e)** $\frac{323}{6}$

Challenge

a) 87 twelfths of pizza were eaten.

b) 86 sixths of cream cake were eaten.

c) $\frac{9}{5}$ of £5 = £9 £9 – £6.50 = £2.50

Relationships between fractions (page 11)

1 a) half as much as **b)** twice as much as
c) twice as much as **d)** twice as much as
e) half as much as **f)** $\frac{1}{4}$ **g)** $\frac{1}{20}$ **h)** $\frac{1}{20}$
i) $\frac{1}{9}$

2 a) $\frac{1}{5}$ **b)** $\frac{3}{8}$ **c)** $\frac{1}{100}$ **d)** $\frac{1}{50}$ **e)** $\frac{1}{12}$

Challenge

a) $\frac{1}{3}$ **b)** $\frac{1}{8}$

Reducing fractions – cancelling (page 13)

1 a) $\frac{3}{4}$ **b)** $\frac{3}{5}$ **c)** $\frac{1}{2}$ **d)** $\frac{1}{4}$ **e)** $\frac{4}{5}$ **f)** $\frac{7}{10}$
g) $\frac{1}{3}$ **h)** $\frac{1}{3}$ **i)** $\frac{1}{3}$ **j)** $\frac{3}{4}$

2 a) $\frac{5}{6}$ **b)** $\frac{5}{13}$ **c)** $\frac{1}{8}$ **d)** $\frac{2}{7}$ **e)** $\frac{23}{36}$

Challenge

Answers will vary. Examples:

a) $\frac{3}{9}, \frac{9}{27}, \frac{10}{30}, \frac{100}{300}, \frac{15}{45}$
b) $\frac{3}{15}, \frac{5}{25}, \frac{15}{75}, \frac{100}{500}, \frac{4}{20}$
c) $\frac{24}{21}, \frac{80}{70}, \frac{56}{49}, \frac{32}{28}, \frac{72}{63}$
d) $\frac{50}{80}, \frac{15}{24}, \frac{20}{32}, \frac{35}{56}, \frac{45}{72}$

Common denominators (page 15)

1 a) $\frac{3}{4}$ **b)** $\frac{8}{9}$ **c)** $\frac{6}{7}$ **d)** $\frac{3}{7}$ **e)** $\frac{4}{5}$
f) > **g)** > **h)** < **i)** < **j)** <

2 a) $\frac{3}{7} \quad \frac{2}{5} \quad \frac{1}{3}$ **b)** $\frac{5}{7} \quad \frac{2}{3} \quad \frac{3}{5}$
c) $\frac{7}{9} \quad \frac{3}{4} \quad \frac{5}{8}$ **d)** $\frac{7}{8} \quad \frac{4}{5} \quad \frac{7}{10}$
e) $\frac{7}{10} \quad \frac{3}{8} \quad \frac{1}{3}$

Challenge

$1\frac{3}{10} \quad 1\frac{5}{6} \quad 2\frac{1}{10} \quad 2\frac{1}{3} \quad 2\frac{2}{5}$

Adding and subtracting fractions with different denominators and mixed numbers (page 17)

1 a) $8\frac{6}{8} = 8\frac{3}{4}$ **b)** $12\frac{5}{7}$ **c)** 12
d) $25\frac{4}{5}$ **e)** 17 **f)** $2\frac{1}{3}$ **g)** $1\frac{2}{3}$
h) $5\frac{3}{4}$ **i)** $2\frac{4}{7}$ **j)** $\frac{3}{5}$ **k)** $1\frac{5}{9}$

2 a) $1\frac{5}{12}$ **b)** $1\frac{1}{16}$ **c)** $1\frac{7}{15}$ **d)** $\frac{1}{12}$
e) $\frac{1}{4}$ **f)** $\frac{3}{10}$

Challenge

$24\frac{11}{16}$

Multiplying simple unit fractions by fractions (page 19)

1 a) $\frac{3}{32}$ **b)** $\frac{2}{21}$ **c)** $\frac{9}{20}$ **d)** $\frac{1}{10}$ **e)** $\frac{7}{48}$

2 a) $\frac{15}{42}$ **b)** $\frac{16}{27}$ **c)** $\frac{7}{15}$ **d)** $\frac{55}{168}$ **e)** $\frac{1}{2}$

3 a) $\frac{5}{9}$ **b)** $\frac{3}{10}$ **c)** $\frac{1}{4}$ **d)** $\frac{1}{40}$ **e)** $\frac{1}{6}$

Challenge

a) $5\frac{1}{4}$ **b)** $12\frac{6}{7}$ **c)** $8\frac{19}{48}$

Dividing proper fractions by whole numbers (page 21)

1 a) $\frac{1}{6}$ **b)** $\frac{2}{15}$ **c)** $\frac{3}{8}$ **d)** $\frac{5}{48}$ **e)** $\frac{1}{63}$ **f)** $\frac{7}{80}$
g) $\frac{3}{30} = \frac{1}{10}$ **h)** $\frac{1}{12} = \frac{1}{14}$ **i)** $\frac{2}{42} = \frac{1}{21}$
j) $\frac{6}{156} = \frac{1}{26}$

2 a) 3 **b)** 4 **c)** 4 **d)** 6

Challenge

$\frac{1}{12}$

Decimal notation (page 23)

1 a) 8.6 **b)** 37.8 **c)** 16.3 **d)** 23.48 **e)** 34.2

f) 74.53 **g)** 52.9 **h)** 108.13 **i)** 71.3

j) 160.22

2 a) 10.966 l **b)** 59.049 kg **c)** 11.468 km

d) 72.427 km **e)** 61.426 kg

Challenge

a) 4.437 km **b)** 2.26 kg **c)** 19.782 l

Decimal and fraction equivalence
(page 25)

1 a) 0.5 **b)** 0.9 **c)** 0.3 **d)** 0.7 **e)** 0.875

f) 0.375 **g)** 0.4 **h)** 0.31 **i)** 0.8 **j)** 0.07

2 a) 0.007 **b)** 0.283 **c)** 0.027 **d)** 0.729

e) 0.107

Challenge

a) $\frac{30}{100} = \frac{3}{10} = 0.3$ **b)** $\frac{35}{100} = \frac{7}{20} = 0.35$

Converting fractions to decimals
using division (page 27)

1 a) 0.5 **b)** 0.75 **c)** 0.25 **d)** 0.4 **e)** 0.2

f) 0.67 **g)** 0.1 **h)** 0.3 **i)** 0.33 **j)** 0.7

2 a) 0.25 **b)** 0.5 **c)** 0.25 **d)** 0.1

Challenge

a) 0.25 **b)** 0.4 **c)** 0.625

Multiplying numbers with up to 2
decimal places (page 29)

1 a) 18.2 **b)** 29.2 **c)** 39.2 **d)** 34.0

e) £44.45 **f)** £41.22 **g)** £45.3

h) 67.56 m **i)** 1131 kg **j)** 771.68 litres

k) 921.2 km

2 a) 5 **b)** 4 **c)** 12.1 **d)** 4.5

Challenge

There are 24 combinations.

There are only 12 different answers.

84, 85, 103.5, 107.5, 124.2, 127.2, 144,

147, 172.8, 176.8, 222.6, 223.6

$23 \times 4.5 = 103.5$ $32 \times 4.5 = 144$

$42 \times 3.5 = 147$ $52 \times 3.4 = 176.8$

$23 \times 5.4 = 124.2$ $32 \times 5.4 = 172.8$

$42 \times 5.3 = 222.6$ $52 \times 4.3 = 223.6$

$24 \times 3.5 = 84$ $34 \times 2.5 = 85$

$43 \times 2.5 = 107.5$ $53 \times 2.4 = 127.2$

$24 \times 5.3 = 127.2$ $34 \times 5.2 = 176.8$

$43 \times 5.2 = 223.6$ $53 \times 4.2 = 222.6$

$25 \times 3.4 = 85$ $35 \times 2.4 = 84$

$45 \times 2.3 = 103.5$ $54 \times 2.3 = 124.2$

$25 \times 4.3 = 107.5$ $35 \times 4.2 = 147$

$45 \times 3.2 = 144$ $54 \times 3.2 = 172.8$

Dividing numbers with up to 2 decimal
places (page 31)

1 a) 0.5 **b)** 0.3 **c)** 0.7 **d)** 0.3 **e)** 1.7 **f)** 3.6

g) 1.7 **h)** 3.5

2 a) 1.76 **b)** 5.36 **c)** 3.42 **d)** 7.23 **e)** 0.18

f) 0.18

Challenge

a) £5.75 **b)** £7.48 **c)** £5.90 **d)** 12

Finding simple percentages of whole numbers and measures (page 33)

1 a) 80p **b)** 22 kg **c)** 240 m **d)** £200 **e)** 40

f) 20 **g)** 80 **h)** 240 **i)** 640 **j)** 200

2 a) 480 metres **b)** £640 **c)** 320 metres

d) £19 **e)** 96 chocolates

Challenge

a) £100,000 **b)** £200,000 **c)** £560,000

Recalling and using equivalences between fractions, decimals and percentages (page 35)

1 a) 62% **b)** 32% **c)** 70% **d)** 45%

e) 97% **f)** $\frac{1}{4}$ = 1:4 = 0.25

g) $\frac{56}{100}$ = 56:100 = 0.56

h) $\frac{8}{100}$ = 8:100 = 0.08

i) $\frac{83}{100}$ = 83:100 = 0.83

j) $\frac{12}{100}$ = 12:100 = 0.12

2 a) 50% **b)** 10% **c)** 70% **d)** 35% **e)** 90%

Challenge

87%

Expressing fractions as percentages (page 37)

1 a) 10% **b)** 25% **c)** 90% **d)** 75% **e)** 50%

f) 33 $\frac{1}{3}$ % **g)** 11% **h)** 66 $\frac{2}{3}$ % **i)** 27%

j) 100%

2 a) $\frac{1}{4}$ and 25% **b)** $\frac{1}{2}$ and 50%

c) $\frac{3}{4}$ and 75% **d)** $\frac{1}{100}$ and 1%

e) $\frac{2}{3}$ and 66 $\frac{2}{3}$%

Challenge

a) Ahmed = 45%, Joe = 22 $\frac{1}{2}$% and

Connor = 32 $\frac{1}{2}$% **b)** Sara had 18%,

Lyn had 15% and Sophie had 17%

A4

Recognising equivalent ratios and reducing ratios (page 39)

1 a) 2:3 **b)** 7:9 **c)** 1:3 **d)** 3:4 **e)** 1:4

f) 1 :10 **g)** 30 cm:100 cm = 3:10

h) 300 cm:25 cm = 12:1

2 a) 4:5 and 12:15 **b)** 10:14 and 5:7

c) 1:3 and 8:24 **d)** 80:100 16:20 and 4:5

3 Possible answers – make sure that each part of the original ratio has been multiplied or divided by the same number.

a) 4:11 16:44 80:220 **b)** 4:14 6:21 20:70

c) 28:46 42:69 70:115 **d)** 12:3 40:10 24:6

Challenge

Alfie will need to add another 15 pears.

Using ratios to show the relative sizes of two quantities (page 41)

1 a) 9 boys **b)** 18 pens **c)** Chantae: 12

books; Namure: 30 books

2 a) 25 marbles **b)** 192 skips

c) Victoria sold 28 cookies;

70 cookies sold in total

d) 48 chairs **e)** 52 books

Challenge

24 cm

Mixed bag – fractions, ratio and proportion (page 43)

1 a) $\frac{1}{3}$ **b)** $\frac{1}{5}$ **c)** $\frac{1}{3}$ **d)** $\frac{1}{6}$ **e)** $\frac{1}{6}$

f) $\frac{1}{4}, \frac{3}{8}, \frac{1}{2}$ **g)** $\frac{2}{7}, \frac{3}{7}, \frac{2}{3}$

h) $\frac{2}{3}, \frac{3}{4}, \frac{5}{6}$ **i)** $\frac{1}{2}, \frac{5}{8}, \frac{13}{16}$

j) $\frac{1}{5}, \frac{3}{10}, \frac{7}{20}$

2 a) 30 **b)** 35 **c)** 12 **d)** 22 **e)** 27

Challenge

a) 45 **b)** 8:4

Blackheath Nursery & Preparatory School
4 St Germans Place
London   SE3 0NJ
020 8858 0692

MATHS DEPARTMENT

1 Complete these calculations.

a) 3.7 + 4.9

b) 33.9 + 3.9

c) 12.8 + 3.5

d) 52.77 – 29.29

e) 47.6 – 13.4

f) 84.5 – 9.97

g) 72.8 – 19.9

h) 28.73 + 79.4

i) 64.7 + 6.6

j) 61.12 + 99.1

2 Complete these calculations of quantities.

a) 4.736 litres + 6.23 litres

b) 62.719 kg – 3.67 kg

c) 8.698 km + 2.77 km

d) 81.2 km – 8.773 km

e) 52.526 kg + 8.9 kg

CHALLENGE

a) Isobel has cycled 18.367 km and Toby has cycled 13.93 km. How much further has Isobel travelled than Toby?

b) Steve has three pumpkins. The first weighs 0.45 kg, the second 0.58 kg and the final one a huge 1.23 kg. How much do his three pumpkins weigh altogether?

c) Tanya has 7.453 litres of red paint. She also has 3.04 litres of blue paint and 9.289 litres of white paint. How much paint does she have altogether?

Decimal and fraction equivalence

Fractions and decimals are related – they are just different ways of writing the same thing.

Look at these decimal and fraction equivalents:

0.5 is the same as $\frac{1}{2}$ 0.1 is the same as $\frac{1}{10}$

0.25 is the same as $\frac{1}{4}$ 0.01 is the same as $\frac{1}{100}$

0.125 is the same as $\frac{1}{8}$ 0.001 is the same as $\frac{1}{1000}$

0.75 is the same as $\frac{3}{4}$

Write $\frac{3}{8}$ as a decimal fraction.

1 *Have another look. Read the question again.*

$\frac{3}{8}$ ... decimal fraction ...

2 *Ask yourself what they want you to find out.*

I need to convert $\frac{3}{8}$ into a decimal.

3 *Look at how you can solve it.*

I know that $\frac{1}{8}$ is the same as 0.125, so $\frac{3}{8}$ is 3 times 0.125.

0.125 × 3 = 0.375

4 *Final answer. Is it correct?*

Yes, 0.375 is correct. It is a little less than a half, as is $\frac{3}{8}$.

---

tips   Hints and tips   Hints and tips   Hints and tips   Hints and tips   Hints and t

- It really helps if you learn as many fraction and decimal equivalents as you can. There are no short cuts – just do it! Start with the list above.
- Other useful ones to learn are:

$\frac{1}{3}$ = 0.333 so $\frac{2}{3}$ = 0.666 and $\frac{1}{5}$ = 0.2 so $\frac{2}{5}$ = 0.4

1 Write these fractions as decimal fractions.

a) $\frac{2}{4}$ [   ]   b) $\frac{9}{10}$ [   ]

c) $\frac{3}{10}$ [   ]   d) $\frac{7}{10}$ [   ]

e) $\frac{7}{8}$ [   ]   f) $\frac{3}{8}$ [   ]

g) $\frac{2}{5}$ [   ]   h) $\frac{31}{100}$ [   ]

i) $\frac{4}{5}$ [   ]   j) $\frac{7}{100}$ [   ]

2 Write these as decimal fractions.

a) $\frac{7}{1000}$ [   ]

b) $\frac{283}{1000}$ [   ]

c) $\frac{27}{1000}$ [   ]

d) $\frac{729}{1000}$ [   ]

e) $\frac{107}{1000}$ [   ]

CHALLENGE

Look at this statement:

$$\frac{800}{1000} = \frac{80}{100} = \frac{8}{10} = 0.8$$

Fill in the blanks.

a) $\frac{300}{1000} = \dfrac{\boxed{}}{\boxed{}} = \dfrac{\boxed{}}{\boxed{}} = \boxed{}.3$

b) $\frac{350}{1000} = \dfrac{\boxed{}}{100} = \dfrac{\boxed{}}{\boxed{}} = \boxed{}.\boxed{}$

Converting fractions to decimals using division

Fractions can be converted into decimals by dividing the top number (the numerator) by the bottom number (the denominator).

You will need a calculator to help you with these questions.

What is three quarters as a decimal fraction?

1 *Have* another look. Read the question again.

Three quarters ... decimal fraction ...

2 *Ask* yourself what they want you to find out.

I need to find out the decimal equivalent of $\frac{3}{4}$.

With my calculator I enter:

My answer is 0.75.

3 *Look* at how you can solve it.

4 *Final* answer. Is it correct?

I know my answer is correct because I remembered $\frac{3}{4} = 0.75$ when I learnt my fraction and decimal equivalents!

---

tips Hints and tips Hints and tips Hints and tips Hints and tips Hints and t

- When you use a calculator, always question what the display tells you. Does it look correct? If not, take a couple of seconds to redo the calculation and press the keys carefully.
- Remember, decimals with whole numbers are the same as mixed fractions, e.g. 2.1 is the same as $2\frac{1}{10}$.

1 Convert these fractions to decimals. See if you can do it without a calculator. (Use one if you have to!)

a) $\frac{1}{2}$

b) $\frac{3}{4}$

c) $\frac{1}{4}$

d) $\frac{2}{5}$

e) $\frac{1}{5}$

f) $\frac{2}{3}$

g) $\frac{1}{10}$

h) $\frac{3}{10}$

i) $\frac{1}{3}$

j) $\frac{7}{10}$

2 Try these word problems. Give your answer as a decimal fraction.

a) In a test, 60 out of 80 cats preferred 'Moggymeat' cat food. What decimal fraction didn't prefer it?

b) McBlobby's burgers are half prime beef and the other half prime grease. What decimal fraction of McBlobby's burgers is prime grease?

c) In Australia, 75 people out of every 100 visit the beach at least once a week. What decimal fraction of people doesn't visit the beach each week?

d) Nine hundred out of a thousand people at a rugby match bought a programme before the game. What decimal fraction of people didn't buy a programme?

CHALLENGE

Without a calculator, work out the following fractions as decimals.

a) $\frac{125}{500}$

b) $\frac{1700}{4250}$

c) $\frac{2825}{4520}$

Multiplying numbers with up to 2 decimal places

When multiplying a decimal number by a whole number it is sometimes easier to change the decimal to a whole number before starting.

What is 3.4 × 6?

1 *Have* another look. Read the question again.

… 3.4 multiplied by 6 …

2 *Ask* yourself what they want you to find out.

I need to find the product of 3.4 and 6. I will estimate an answer by rounding the decimal number to the nearest whole number: 3.4 rounded is 3. So 3 × 6 = 18. So 3.4 × 6 will be just over 18.

3 *Look* at how you can solve it.

Step 1 I will multiply 3.4 by 10 to make it a whole number: 34 × 6 =

Step 2 Use your preferred method for multiplication. You could complete this calculation by using partitioning and jotting down the answer to each stage.

Step 3 Divide the answer by 10 (we multiplied the original decimal number by 10 at the start). So 3.4 × 6 = 20.4

4 *Final* answer. Is it correct?

Yes. I have repeated my calculation and got the same answer. I have checked my answer against my original estimate and it is very close.

---

tips   **Hints and tips   Hints and tips   Hints and tips   Hints and tips   Hints and t**

- When you multiply a decimal number by a whole number, the answer will have the same number of digits after the decimal point as in the question.

E.g. 1.2 × 6 = 7.2   There is one digit after the decimal point in 1.2 and there is one digit after the decimal point in the answer 7.2.

1 Multiply these decimals by whole numbers.

a) 2.6 × 7

b) 7.3 × 4

c) 4.9 × 8

d) 6.8 × 5

e) £6.35 × 7

f) £4.58 × 9

g) £9.06 × 5

h) 5.63 m × 12

i) 45.24 kg × 25

j) 55.12 litres × 14

k) 26.32 km × 35

2 Use a calculator to work out the missing number in these sentences.

a) 5.65 × [ ] = 28.25

b) 9.7 × [ ] = 38.8

c) [ ] × 7 = 84.7

d) [ ] × 25 = 112.5

CHALLENGE

By using the digits 2, 3, 4 and 5 to make two-digit whole numbers and two-digit numbers to one decimal place, how many different products can you make?

E.g. 2.3 × 45 = 103.5   2.4 × 35 = 84

How will you know when you have made all of the different combinations of two-digit whole numbers and two-digit decimal numbers? (Hint: Work systematically.)

Dividing numbers with up to 2 decimal places

When dividing a decimal number by a whole number, it is often easier to divide if you change the decimal to a whole number before you start.

$5.67 \div 6$ would become $567 \div 6 = 94.5$. So $5.67 \div 6 = 0.945$

What is $3.54 \div 6$?

1 *Have* another look. Read the question again.

… 3.54 divided by 6 …

2 *Ask* yourself what they want you to find out.

If I divide 3.54 into six equal groups, what would the value of each group be? I will estimate an answer first by rounding the decimal number to the nearest whole number: 3.54 rounded is 4. So $4 \div 6$ will give an answer of less than 1.

3 *Look* at how you can solve it.

Step 1 Change 3.54 into a whole number by multiplying it by 100.

Step 2 Carry out the division.

Step 3 Divide the answer by 100. So the final answer is $59 \div 100 = 0.59$

4 *Final* answer. Is it correct?

I have repeated my calculation and got the same answer. I have checked by using the inverse operation.

tips Hints and tips Hints and tips Hints and tips Hints and tips Hints and t

- When dividing numbers to two decimal places, it is useful to think of the number as an amount of money being shared between a group of children.

1 Divide these decimals by whole numbers.

a) 4.5 ÷ 9

b) 0.6 ÷ 2

c) 4.9 ÷ 7

d) 2.4 ÷ 8

e) 20.4 ÷ 12

f) 50.4 ÷ 14

g) 28.9 ÷ 17

h) 87.5 ÷ 25

2 Now try these.

a) 10.56 ÷ 6

b) 16.08 ÷ 3

c) 27.36 ÷ 8

d) 36.15 ÷ 5

e) 3.42 ÷ 19

f) 2.52 ÷ 14

CHALLENGE

a) D'Shaun has put together fifteen party bags for his friends. If he spent £86.25 in total, how much did each bag of goodies cost?

b) Esha buys eight dictionaries for fifty-nine pounds and eighty-four pence in total. How much did each dictionary cost?

c) Twenty-five children win a prize of £147.50. If the money is shared out equally, how much will each child receive?

d) Aaliyah has just spent £40.80 on a pen for each of her friends. Each pen cost £3.40. How many friends did Aaliyah buy pens for?

Finding simple percentages of whole numbers and measures

Finding a percentage of a quantity is useful when dealing with money.

To find 10% of something you have to divide it by 10.

$$10\% \text{ of } 50 = 5$$

You can then use doubling to find other percentages.

$$20\% \text{ of } 50 = 10$$

$$40\% \text{ of } 50 = 20, \text{ etc.}$$

What is the price of this car after a 20% discount?

1 *Have* another look. Read the question again.

£500 … 20% off …

2 *Ask* yourself what they want you to find out.

I need to find 20% of £500 and then subtract that from £500.

3 *Look* at how you can solve it.

10% of 500 is 500 ÷ 10 = 50

So 20% of 500 = 100 (50 doubled)

£500 − £100 = £400

4 *Final* answer. Is it correct?

The price of the car after a 20% discount is £400. I also know that $20\% = \frac{1}{5}$ and $\frac{1}{5}$ of 500 = 100.

tips   Hints and tips   Hints and tips   Hints and tips   Hints and tips   Hints and t

- You can use halving to help you find 5%. Find 10% first and then halve the answer. This means you can add the 5%s and the 10%s together to find 15%, 25%, 35%, etc.
- To find 1% of a quantity, first find 10% and then find 10% of that answer. You can now find the percentage of any quantity by adding all the 10%s, 5%s and 1%s together!

1 Try these to warm up!

a) Find 10% of £8.

b) Find 10% of 220 kg.

c) Find 10% of £50.

d) Calculate 20% of 400 litres.

e) What is 20% of 200?

f) How much is 40% of 50?

g) What is 40% of 200?

h) Work out 80% of 300 metres.

i) What is 80% of 800?

j) Find 40% of £500.

2 Now try these word problems.

a) There are 25 children in Class 6. If 20% of them are off sick, how many children remain?

b) Frank has £800 to spend on a car. He only spends 80% of his money. How much does Frank spend?

c) Ann-Marie has to travel 800 metres to school. She rides 40% of the distance on her scooter and walks the rest. How far does Ann-Marie walk?

d) Martin wants to give 10% of his savings to his favourite charity. He has saved £190. How much does Martin give to charity?

e) Phoebe ate 80% of a box of chocolates which contained 120 chocolates! How many chocolates did Phoebe eat?

CHALLENGE

The pop star Normandy Shields made £1,000,000 from her first hit – 'Whoops, I've Lost My Bloomers!' She paid 10% to her agent, 20% to her manager and spent 80% of what was left on clothes.

a) How much did her agent receive?

b) How much did Normandy give her manager?

c) How much did Normandy spend on clothes?

Recalling and using equivalences between fractions, decimals and percentages

The word 'percent' means 'parts per hundred'. We use the % symbol for percent.

Draw a grid of a hundred squares. Now shade seventy-three squares. The ratio of the *number of shaded squares* to the *total number of squares* can be shown as a fraction.

Ratio ➜ 73:100   Fraction ➜ $\frac{73}{100}$

We can show this fraction as a percentage by adding % ➜ 73%

Write 10% as a fraction, ratio and decimal.

1 | Have another look. Read the question again. | 10% ... fraction ... ratio ... decimal.

2 | Ask yourself what they want you to find out. | I need to write 10% as a fraction, ratio and decimal.

3 | Look at how you can solve it. | 10% as a fraction = $\frac{10}{100}$ which is $\frac{1}{10}$.

10% as a ratio is 10 to 100 or 1:10.

10% as a decimal is 0.10 or .1.

4 | Final answer. Is it correct? | Yes, I have given the three answers that are required.

- Percentages can be used to show the results of surveys or marks scored in a test.
You can work them out easily with a calculator. '77 out of 220 people asked said they liked anchovies on pizza.' That is $\frac{77}{220}$ as a fraction. To turn it into a percentage key in:

7 7 ÷ 2 2 0 %

You will have the answer 35 which means 35% of the people asked liked anchovies on their pizza!

1 Write these as a percentage.

a) $\frac{62}{100}$ ☐   b) 0.32 ☐   c) $\frac{7}{10}$ ☐

d) 45:100 ☐   e) 0.97 ☐

Write each percentage as a fraction, ratio and decimal.

	Fraction	Ratio	Decimal			Fraction	Ratio	Decimal
f) 25%				g) 56%				
h) 8%				i) 83%				
j) 12%								

2 What percentage of these patterns has been shaded?

a) ☐   b) ☐   c) ☐

d) ☐   e) ☐

CHALLENGE

What percentage of this stadium is full of spectators for the Normandy Shields concert?

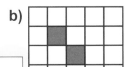

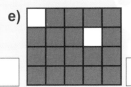

35

Expressing fractions as percentages

Fractions can be written as percentages. You need to learn these fraction/percentage equivalents.

$\frac{1}{2}$ = 50% $\frac{1}{4}$ = 25% $\frac{3}{4}$ = 75%

$\frac{1}{3}$ is nearly 33% ($33\frac{1}{3}$%) $\frac{2}{3}$ is nearly 66% ($66\frac{2}{3}$%)

$\frac{1}{10}$ = 10% $\frac{1}{100}$ = 1%

Write $\frac{7}{10}$ as a percentage.

1 *Have* another look. Read the question again.

$\frac{7}{10}$ as a percentage …

2 *Ask* yourself what they want you to find out.

I need to find the percentage equivalent of $\frac{7}{10}$.

3 *Look* at how you can solve it.

Look at the information above …

$\frac{1}{10}$ = 10%

So $\frac{7}{10}$ is 7 × 10% = 70%

4 *Final* answer. Is it correct?

Yes, $\frac{7}{10}$ is the same as 70%.

My answer also *looks* correct.

tips   Hints and tips   Hints and tips   Hints and tips   Hints and tips   Hints and t

- Learn the fraction and percentage equivalents as you would your number bonds and multiplication facts.
- Other useful fraction/percentage equivalents are:

$\frac{1}{5}$ = 20% $\frac{2}{5}$ = 40% $\frac{3}{5}$ = 60% $\frac{4}{5}$ = 80% $\frac{1}{8}$ = 12 % $\frac{3}{8}$ = 37 %

1 Write the percentage equivalents of these fractions. Use the information on the previous page to help you.

a) $\frac{1}{10}$ [ ] b) $\frac{2}{8}$ [ ]

c) $\frac{9}{10}$ [ ] d) $\frac{6}{8}$ [ ]

e) $\frac{5}{10}$ [ ] f) $\frac{3}{9}$ [ ]

g) $\frac{11}{100}$ [ ] h) $\frac{6}{9}$ [ ]

i) $\frac{27}{100}$ [ ] j) $\frac{1}{1}$ [ ]

2 Reduce these fractions to their lowest form and write their percentage equivalent.

a) $\frac{18}{72}$ [ ]

b) $\frac{250}{500}$ [ ]

c) $\frac{48}{64}$ [ ]

d) $\frac{10}{1000}$ [ ]

e) $\frac{54}{81}$ [ ]

CHALLENGE

a) Ahmed, Joe and Connor were collecting stickers. Out of a total of 1000 stickers, Ahmed had 450, Joe had 225 and Connor had 325. What percentage did each have of the total?

[ ]

b) Lyn, Sara and Sophie shared their sweets. Out of a total of 200 sweets, Sara had 36, Lyn had 30 and Sophie had 34. What percentage did each have of the total?

[ ]

Recognising equivalent ratios and reducing ratios

Two or more ratios that have the same value are called equivalent ratios or equal ratios.

white:blue
1:4

white:blue
2:8

These are equivalent ratios. They represent the same relationship between the white and blue squares. For every one white square there are four blue ones. Reduce ratios to their lowest terms – this will make it far easier to see if they are equivalent.

Which of the following ratios is equivalent to 2:3? 5:15   12:18

1 *Have* another look. Read the question again.

Which … ratios are equivalent …

2 *Ask* yourself what they want you to find out.

Which of these ratios have the same value?

3 *Look* at how you can solve it.

I can reduce each ratio by finding the highest common factor for each part of the ratio and dividing, like this: 5:15. The highest common factor of 5 and 15 is 5.
5 ÷ 5 = 1   15 ÷ 5 = 3   So 5:15 = 1:3
12:18   The highest common factor of 12 and 18 is 6.
12 ÷ 6 = 2 18 ÷ 6 = 3   So 12:18 = 2:3

4 *Final* answer. Is it correct?

I have repeated my calculations.

tips   Hints and tips   Hints and tips   Hints and tips   Hints and tips   Hints and t

• Knowing your times tables will help you to spot highest common factors quickly.

1 Reduce these ratios to their lowest terms.

a) 16:24   **b)** 63:81

c) 24:72   **d)** 45:60

e) 75:300   **f)** 16 cm:160 cm

Hint: Change the metres into centimetres.

g) 30 cm:2 m   **h)** 3 m:25 cm

2 Circle the ratios that are equivalent to each other. (Hint: It is easier to compare them if you reduce them to their lowest terms.)

a) 4:5   6:12   2:7   8:12   12: 15

b) 6:8   10:14   7:21   5:7   4:12

c) 1:16   1:3   8:24   2:12

d) 80:100   8:80   16:20   4:5

3 Make three ratios that are equivalent to each of the following.

a) 8:22

b) 2:7

c) 14:23

d) 120:30

CHALLENGE

Alfie says that the ratio of apples to pears is 3:2. There are 25 fruits altogether. If Alfie doubles the number of apples, how many pears will he need to add to keep the ratio of apples to pears the same? (Hint: Model the problem by showing the ratio 3:2 using squares.)

A	A	A	P	P	25

Using ratios to show the relative sizes of two quantities

A ratio compares values. It tells you how much of one thing there is compared to something else. You may be asked to find one or two quantities, the difference between the quantities or the total.

If Thom's cake has a ratio of 1 part margarine to 2 parts flour and a mass of 450 g before other ingredients, what is the mass of flour used?

1 *Have* another look. Read the question again.

What is the mass of flour used in Thom's cake?

2 *Ask* yourself what they want you to find out.

I need to *compare* the amount of flour to margarine.

If there are 2 parts of flour and 1 part of margarine, there are 3 parts altogether.

| F | F | M | = 450g

The total mass of the flour and margarine is 450 g. I will find the mass of part by dividing the total mass by 3.

450 g ÷ 3 = 150 g

So the mass of 1 part is 150 g.

| 150 g | 150 g | 150 g |

There are 2 parts of flour. So the mass of the flour is 150 g × 2 = 300 g

3 *Look* at how you can solve it.

4 *Final* answer. Is it correct?

Yes. I have repeated my calculation and got the same answer.

tips   Hints and tips   Hints and tips   Hints and tips   Hints and tips   Hints and t

- It can be really useful to model the problem by drawing boxes for each part described in the ratio, just like in the example above.

1

a) In Aquamarine Class the ratio of girls to boys is 3:1. If there are 36 children in the class, how many boys are there?

Use this diagram to help you to model the problem.

girls	girls	girls	boys

= .... children in total

b) Bethany and Andrew share felt-tipped pens in the ratio 1:4. If there are 30 pens altogether, how many fewer pens did Bethany get than Andrew?

c) Chantae and Namure have 42 books between them. The ratio of the number of books owned by Chantae and Namure is 2:5. How many books does each child have?

2

Use the ratios in these word problems to work out the actual amounts.

a) Kai and Aran share marbles in the ratio 3:5. If Kai has 15 marbles, how many does Aran have?

b) Mya and Cameron are in a skipping competition. They skip at a ratio of 5:8. If Mya skips 120 times in one minute, how many times does Cameron skip in the same amount of time?

c) For every 3 cookies that Estelle sells, Victoria sells 2. Estelle sold 42 cookies. How many cookies did Victoria sell?

d) Millie and Seth put chairs out in the hall. For every 4 chairs that Seth puts out, Millie puts out 7. If Millie puts out 84 chairs, how many chairs does Seth put out?

e) Minka and Dante love reading. For every 5 books that Minka reads, Dante reads 8. If Dante reads 32 books, how many books did they read altogether?

CHALLENGE

The scale on a map is 8 cm:4 km. If the distance between two cities is 12 km, how far apart are the two cities on the map? (Hint: Reduce the ratio to its lowest terms before calculating the distance.)

Mixed bag – fractions, ratio and proportion

On the right-hand page there is a mixture of questions. You will need to use everything you have learnt so far to solve these problems. Look back through the book for help if you need it. Remember to put in the units!

Reduce this fraction to its simplest form: $\frac{16}{96}$

1 *Have* another look. Read the question again.

Reduce ... simplest form.

2 *Ask* yourself what they want you to find out.

What is the easiest way of presenting this fraction?

3 *Look* at how you can solve it.

What is the highest number that divides into 16 and 96? OK, let's try 8. Two 8s are 16 and twelve 8s are 96. So that gives me $\frac{2}{12}$. I can simplify this further by dividing the top and bottom by 2. My final answer is $\frac{1}{6}$.

4 *Final* answer. Is it correct?

$\frac{1 \times 16}{6 \times 16} = \frac{16}{96}$

tips   **Hints and tips**   **Hints and tips**   **Hints and tips**   **Hints and tips**   **Hints and t**

• Always approach the problem step-by-step.

• Draw pictures to help you make sense of the problem.

1 Reduce these fractions to their simplest form.

Order these fractions on a number line.

a) $\frac{4}{12}$

b) $\frac{8}{40}$

c) $\frac{15}{45}$

d) $\frac{20}{120}$

e) $\frac{9}{54}$

f) $\frac{3}{8}$ $\frac{1}{4}$ $\frac{1}{2}$

g) $\frac{2}{7}$ $\frac{2}{3}$ $\frac{3}{7}$

h) $\frac{2}{3}$ $\frac{5}{6}$ $\frac{3}{4}$

i) $\frac{13}{16}$ $\frac{5}{8}$ $\frac{1}{2}$

j) $\frac{1}{5}$ $\frac{3}{10}$ $\frac{7}{20}$

2 Find the fractions of these numbers.

a) $\frac{2}{3}$ of 45

b) $\frac{5}{8}$ of 56

c) $\frac{1}{7}$ of 84

d) $\frac{2}{25}$ of 275

e) $\frac{3}{11}$ of 99

CHALLENGE

a) There are 180 biscuits in my tin. There are 3 custard creams for every 9 bourbons. How many custard creams are there in the tin?

b) What is the ratio of blue squares to white squares in this pattern?

The Skills Builders Range

Grammar and Punctuation

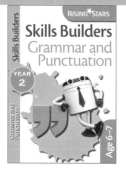   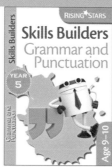 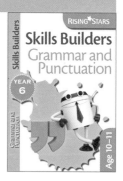

Spelling and Vocabulary

 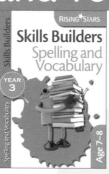 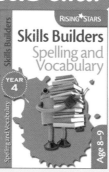 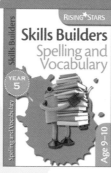 

Times Tables

Fractions, Decimals and Percentages

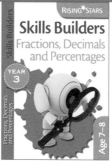 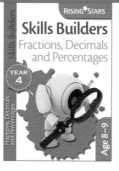 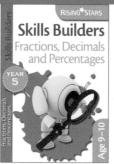 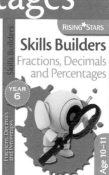